Guest Spot

FILM THEMES
Playalong *for* Flute

GW00566934

WISE PUBLICATIONS
London/New York/Paris/Sydney/Copenhagen/Madrid

Exclusive Distributors:
Music Sales Limited
8/9 Frith Street, London W1V 5TZ, England.
Music Sales Pty Limited
120 Rothschild Avenue, Rosebery, NSW 2018, Australia.

Order No. AM941875
ISBN 0-7119-6256-1
This book © Copyright 1998 by Wise Publications.

Book design by Michael Bell Design.
Music arranged by Jack Long.
Music processed by Enigma Music Production Services.
Cover photography by George Taylor.
Printed in the United Kingdom by Page Bros., Norwich, Norfolk.

CD recorded by Paul Honey.
Instrumental solos by Bill Whelan.
All keyboards and programming by Paul Honey.

Your Guarantee of Quality:
As publishers, we strive to produce every book to
the highest commercial standards.
The music has been freshly engraved and the book has been
carefully designed to minimise awkward page turns and
to make playing from it a real pleasure.
Particular care has been given to specifying acid-free, neutral-sized
paper made from pulps which have not been elemental chlorine bleached.
This pulp is from farmed sustainable forests and was
produced with special regard for the environment.
Throughout, the printing and binding have been planned to
ensure a sturdy, attractive publication which should give years of enjoyment.
If your copy fails to meet our high standards,
please inform us and we will gladly replace it.

Music Sales' complete catalogue describes thousands of
titles and is available in full colour sections by subject,
direct from Music Sales Limited.
Please state your areas of interest and send a
cheque/postal order for £1.50 for postage to:
Music Sales Limited, Newmarket Road, Bury St. Edmunds, Suffolk IP33 3YB.

Visit the Internet Music Shop at
http://www.musicsales.co.uk

Fingering Guide

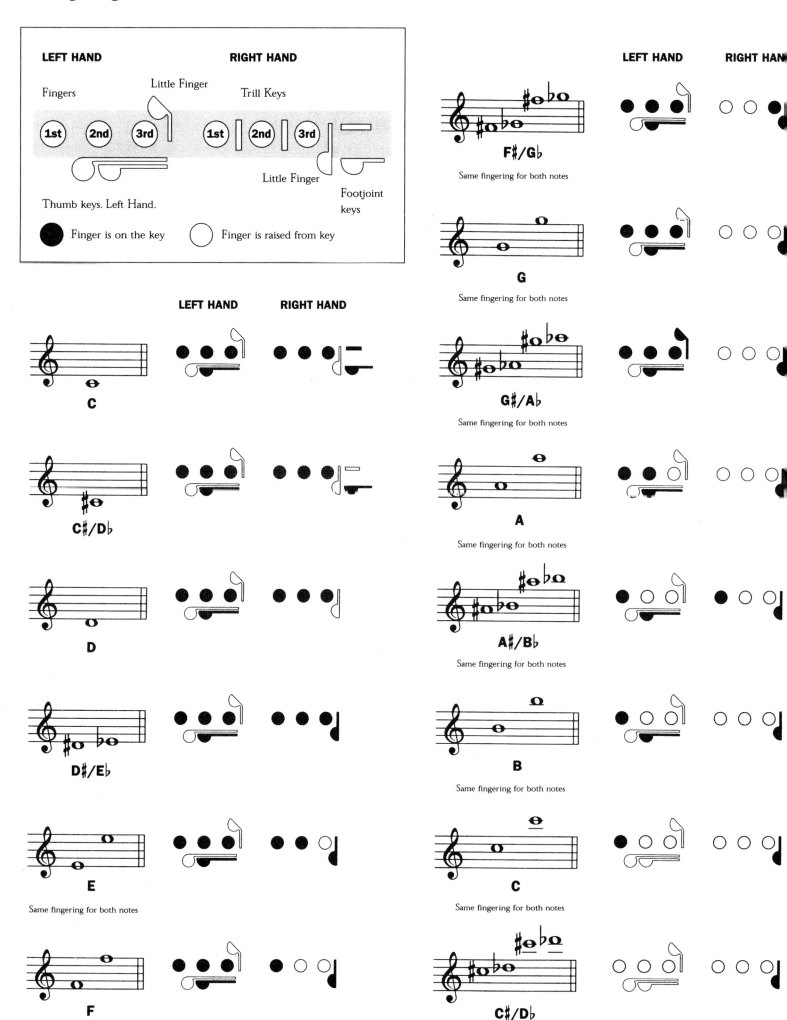

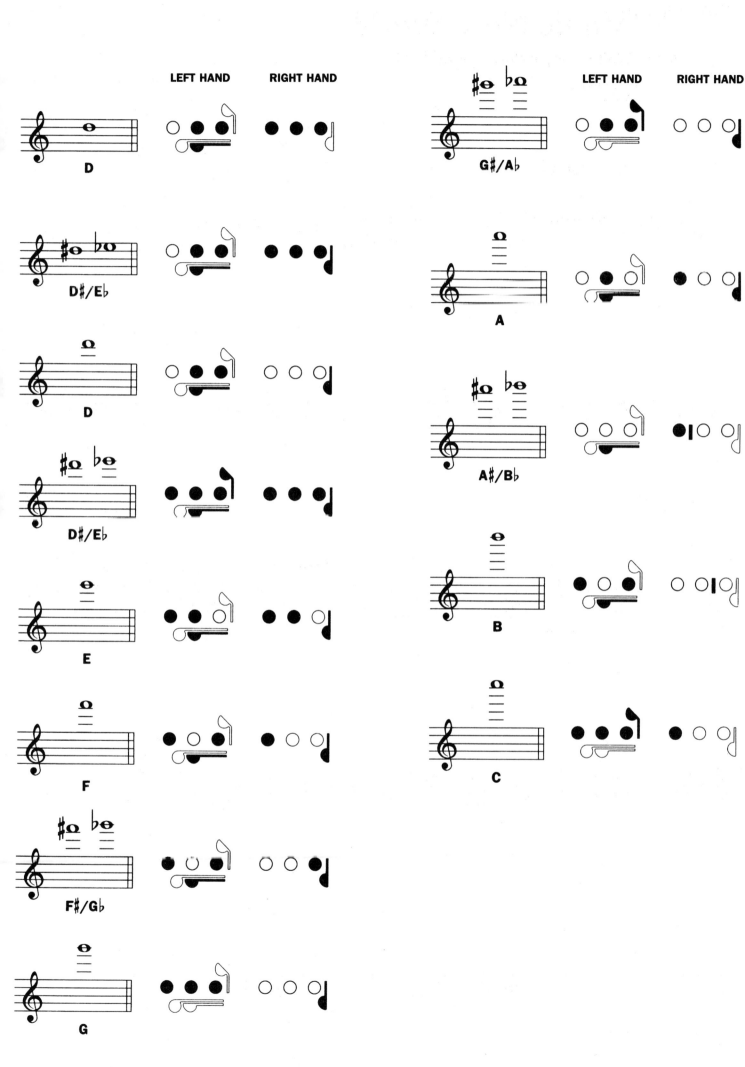

A Whole New World

(From Walt Disney Pictures' "Aladdin")

Music by Alan Menken
Lyrics by Tim Rice

Medium tempo ($\quad$ = 110)

Circle Of Life

(From Walt Disney Pictures' "The Lion King")

Music by Elton John
Lyrics by Tim Rice

Slow medium ($\quarternote = 88$)

To ⊕ *Coda*

D. 𝄋 *al Coda*

⊕ **CODA**

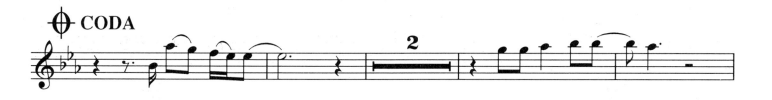

rall.

Where Do I Begin

(Theme from Love Story)

Music by Francis Lai
Words by Carl Sigman

Medium slow (♩ = 76)

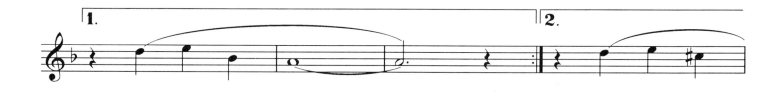

D. %S al Coda

CODA

Love Is All Around

Words & Music by Reg Presley

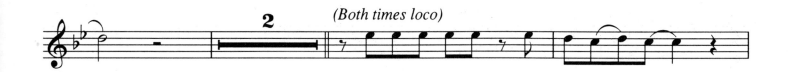

(Both times loco)

Moon River

Music by Henry Mancini
Words by Johnny Mercer

Medium slow (♩ = 84)

D. %: al Coda

CODA

rall.

Schindler's List

By John Williams

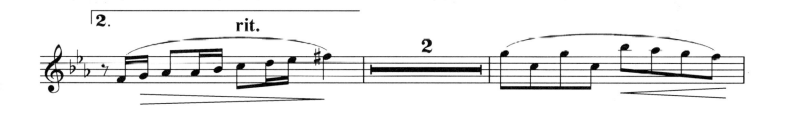

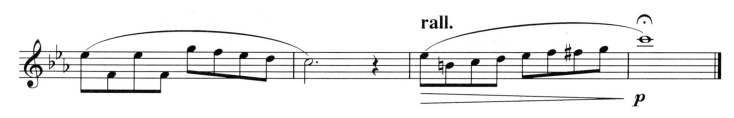

Theme from The Godfather

By Nino Rota

Up Where We Belong

Words & Music by Jack Nitzsche, Will Jennings & Buffy Sainte Marie

Medium slow ♩ = 70

You Must Love Me

Music by Andrew Lloyd Webber
Lyrics by Tim Rice

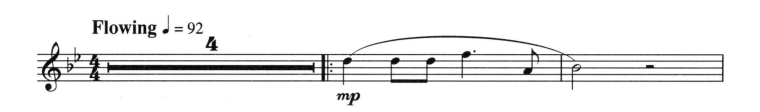

Take My Breath Away

Words by Tom Whitlock
Music by Giorgio Moroder

D. %. al Coda

CODA

3

rit.

32